Acknowledgements
The Starblazer Team would like to give special thanks
to Grant Morrison, Mick McMahon,
Keith Robson, Ian Kennedy, Enrique Alcatena,
D. Broadbent, Christopher Murray, the DC Thomson
Operations Department, Iain McKenzie,
the DC Thomson Archive Department and the
DC Thomson Media Administration Department

The Starblazer Team
Editorial
Georgia Battle, Kate McAuliffe,
Michelle O'Donnell, Gordon Tait, Rhiannon Tate

Designer
Grant Wood

Design Editor
Leon Strachan

Editor-in-Chief
Alexandria Turner

Children's Publisher
Gareth Whelan

Head of Magazines
Maria T. Welch

Cover by Neil Roberts
Endpapers by Grant Wood

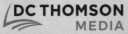

Published in Great Britain by DC Thomson & Co. Ltd.,
2 Albert Square, Dundee, DD1 1DD.

© DC Thomson & Co., Ltd. 2019.

This volume collects material originally published in Starblazer
issues #45 from 1981 and #71 from 1982.

Email: generalenquiries@commandomag.com

www.commandocomics.com

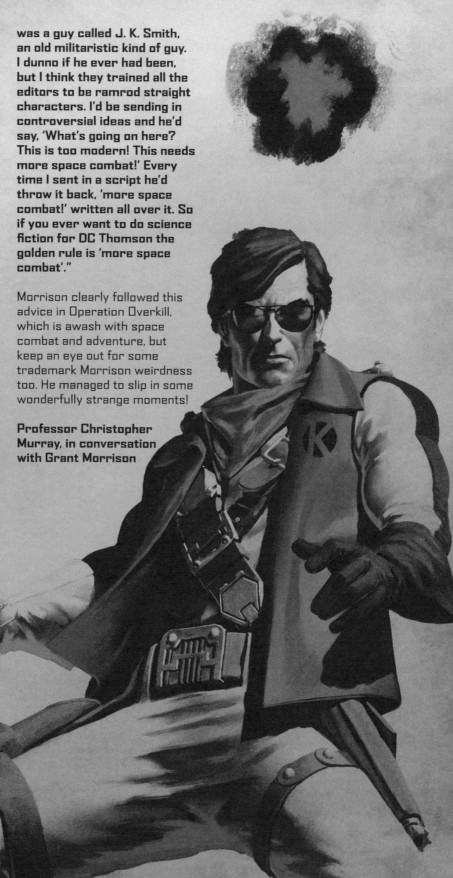

Grant Morrison is one of the most acclaimed writers of comics in the world, but few know that some of his earliest professional work was for DC Thomson.
As he recalls:

"I actually never came to Dundee. The *Starblazer* editors would come down and meet me in Queen Street station in Glasgow. It was like one of those Soviet spy kind of things where they would meet up and push a brown envelope across the desk. Those guys basically taught me how to write comic books. They showed me how comic scripts were laid out. They showed me the basics of beginnings, middles and ends that you really have to know up front. They have a very ancient style that they've been using since 31AD or something, and it's really sound, so they taught me everything I know about the technical side of writing comics. The editor I dealt with was a guy called J. K. Smith, an old militaristic kind of guy. I dunno if he ever had been, but I think they trained all the editors to be ramrod straight characters. I'd be sending in controversial ideas and he'd say, 'What's going on here? This is too modern! This needs more space combat!' Every time I sent in a script he'd throw it back, 'more space combat!' written all over it. So if you ever want to do science fiction for DC Thomson the golden rule is 'more space combat'."

Morrison clearly followed this advice in Operation Overkill, which is awash with space combat and adventure, but keep an eye out for some trademark Morrison weirdness too. He managed to slip in some wonderfully strange moments!

Professor Christopher Murray, in conversation with Grant Morrison

SPACE FICTION ADVENTURE IN PICTURES:

A BRIEF HISTORY OF A COSMIC COMIC!

Blasting onto newsagent shelves forty years ago, DC Thomson's *Starblazer* featured otherworldly adventures through space and time — all in a digest size that fit nicely in your jacket pocket. Longer than DC Thomson's other comic pocketbooks, like *Commando*, each *Starblazer* was sixty-four black-and-white interior pages of planet-hopping Science Fiction ventures, all working as a stand-alone story, while some stellar series were developed from its roguish recurring characters. All of this was wrapped nicely in an outlandish full-colour painted cover which usually presented alien warriors, titanic spacecraft, and glimpses of far-off worlds.

First launched in April 1979, *Starblazer* was the brainchild of *Sparky* Editor, Ian Chisholm, and Jack Smith (who would become the title's Editor), both of whom were interested in creating Science Fiction tales for DC Thomson. The timing was perfect for the genre, as it was released two years after the sensational popularity of *Star Wars* (which later earned the subtitle *A New Hope*), and would rival British Science Fiction comic, *2000 AD*.

Early issues followed typical space opera tropes and conventions set by the likes of Science Fiction comics 'Buck Rogers in the 25th Century A.D.' and 'Flash Gordon', so space battles and arena fights against killer robots and extra-terrestrial predators were never far from hand. This progressed through time to darker material and the more complex subjects of class divides, slavery, and other consequences of power imbalances in galactic colonialism as the title established its more mature space adventure footing.

However, by 1986 the public's tastes were changing and issue 168, 'Timeslay', evolved *Starblazer*'s tagline from 'Space Fiction Adventure in Pictures' to 'Fantasy Fiction in Pictures' following the rising popularity of the Fantasy genre. But, despite the change of subtitle, Science Fiction still prevailed as the heart of the publication and titles such as 'The Cyborg Chaser', 'The Robot Kid' and 'Lord of the Far Planet' could still be seen amidst the likes of 'Dragon Slayer' and 'The Power of the Warlocks'. Of course, Fantasy and Science Fiction genres often walk hand in hand, especially at a time when space wizards were seen duelling with light swords on cinema screens — and *Starblazer* was no different.

Significant in the publication's history for another reason, 'Timeslay' was also the first issue to feature a wraparound cover, by none other than British comic art legend, Ian Kennedy, who already had several covers under his belt for not only *Starblazer* but many of DC Thomson's other comic titles. Furthermore, Kennedy isn't the only big-name alumni to work on the title. Some of comic writer Grant Morrison's earliest work is on the pages of *Starblazer*, his first issue being No. 15, 'Algol the Terrible', (which he penned and drew) when *Starblazer* was still in its first year of publication. Morrison penned several issues after this, even creating the outlaw character Mikal R Kayn, who appeared in sixteen issues including the featured 'Operation Overkill'. Also gracing *Starblazer*'s pages is artwork by illustrator Mick McMahon, whose other notable works include the title *2000 AD*, adding his instantly recognisable style to 'Jaws of Death'.

By January 1991, *Starblazer* had reached its 281st and final issue, closing the portal to DC Thomson's Science Fiction Picture Library. However, the title lived on as it was resurrected in 2007 as a digital role-playing game by Cubicle 7 Entertainment, immersing the players as they took the helm in their own space adventures.

Now, forty years on, like the Science Fiction genre itself, *Starblazer* is back once more, here reformatting two classic stories into graphic novel size with a brand new wraparound cover by British comic artist and genre enthusiast Neil Roberts. And beyond this? Who knows what mysteries the galaxy holds for *Starblazer*...

STARBLAZER No.22 - 'The Pirates of Vega III' Ian Kennedy. (1980).

OPERATION OVERKILL

ORBITING THE RED STAR
LUYTEN 726-8A WAS THE EARTH
ALLIANCE'S GIANT TOP SECURITY PRISON. WITHIN
ITS WALLS WERE SOME OF THE GALAXY'S MOST VICIOUS
CRIMINALS. NO-ONE HAD EVER ESCAPED ITS CONFINES . . .

ON BOARD, A NEW WARDEN CHECKED IN.

IS THIS ALTA THE SAME ONE WHO WIPED OUT THE ALIOTH SYSTEM?

THAT'S HIM. HE ENSLAVED FOUR OTHER SYSTEMS BEFORE THE ALLIANCE MANAGED TO BRING HIM DOWN.

EACH PRISONER HAD A SERVOROB — A ROBOTIC TURNKEY THAT CATERED FOR PRISONERS IN SOLITARY.

THIS IS HIS CELL. COME ON, ALTA! WHAT'S WRONG WITH THE SERVOROB . . .

THE GUARD NEVER FOUND OUT — A BLAST OF WHITE HOT FLAME HIT HIM.

THE ALARM! GOT TO REACH . . . SERVOROB HAS MALFUNCTIONED.

THE SECOND GUARD WAS TOO SLOW.

... AND THE RELEASED PRISONERS SWARMED IN.

ALTA CLIMBED INTO THE COCKPIT. . .

. . . OPENED THE AIRLOCK AND BLASTED OFF.

GOODBYE, FOOLS. I HAVE NO NEED OF YOU NOW.

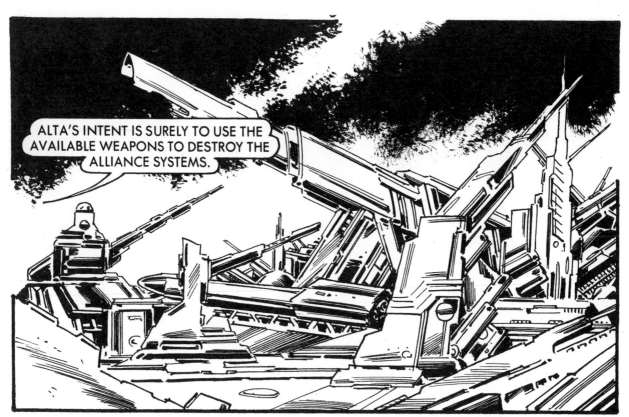

NOT IMPOSSIBLE. IN FACT I HAVE ALREADY BEEN THROUGH THE STARHAMMER — SEVEN YEARS AGO!

I WAS AIDED BY A FRIEND — A BERNIAN BIOLOGIST NAMED SHADE. THE STARHAMMER IS NOT COMPOSED OF ORDINARY MINERALS . . . THESE ARE LIVING CREATURES! IT IS POSSIBLE TO REGISTER THEIR THOUGHT PATTERNS. SHADE INVENTED A MACHINE WHICH COULD READ THESE PATTERNS. IT IS POSSIBLE TO TRANSMIT WARNINGS AND THE CREATURES MAKE WAY.

THE NEXT DAY AT DAWN, KAYN'S SHIP LIFTED OFF.

HE WAS COMPLETELY UNPREPARED FOR THE SCENE OF DESTRUCION HE SUDDENLY FACED.

KAYN TOUCHED DOWN AND SURVEYED THE CARNAGE.

UNBELIEVABLE! ALTA HAS TO BE STOPPED.

HIS FIRST BLAST CRIPPLED ONE OF THE ENEMY SHIPS.

GIVE ME A LIFEFORM SCAN . . . AND A PROBABLE DESTINATION.

THREE HABITABLE PLANETS ARE WITHIN REASONABLE DISTANCES . . . THRYMHEIM, WOLFHOLT, GALLA . . . SCAN SHOWS THREE MEN TO EACH SHIP. ALL IN THEIR PROPER STATIONS . . . PILOT, NAVIGATOR, WEAPONS TECHNICIAN . . . NO OTHERS . . .

THEN SHADE ISN'T ABOARD THOSE SHIPS. DEFENCE PROCEDURES! HERE THEY COME!

SIMULTANEOUS ACTIVATION OF SONIC CANNON AND LASERS — FIRE.

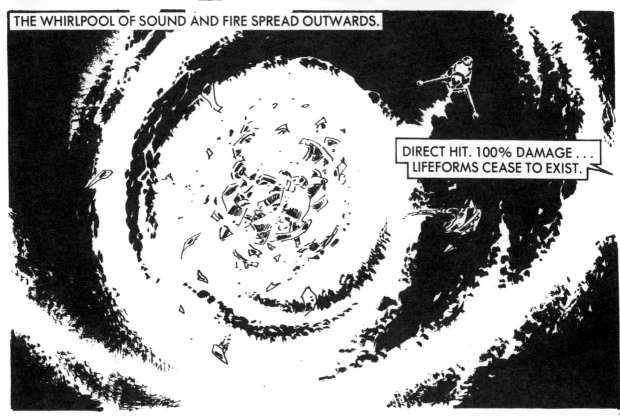

THE WHIRLPOOL OF SOUND AND FIRE SPREAD OUTWARDS.

DIRECT HIT. 100% DAMAGE . . . LIFEFORMS CEASE TO EXIST.

KAYN WARPED INTO WOLFHOLT AIRSPACE, PASSING THE MANY ALIENS WHO FLITTED FROM ONE REFUGE TO ANOTHER.

WOLFHOLT WAS ONE OF THE MANY LAWLESS WORLDS WHERE FEW HONEST PEOPLE WERE BRAVE ENOUGH TO APPROACH.

INFORMATION

KAYN LANDED IN THE SPACEPORT.

EVERYBODY COMING IN HERE IS VIDEOGRAPHED AND LOGGED . . . SO IF SHADE'S HERE, I'LL KNOW.

KAYN'S NEVRON PHASER BLASTED THE OTHER KILLER THROUGH A WALL.

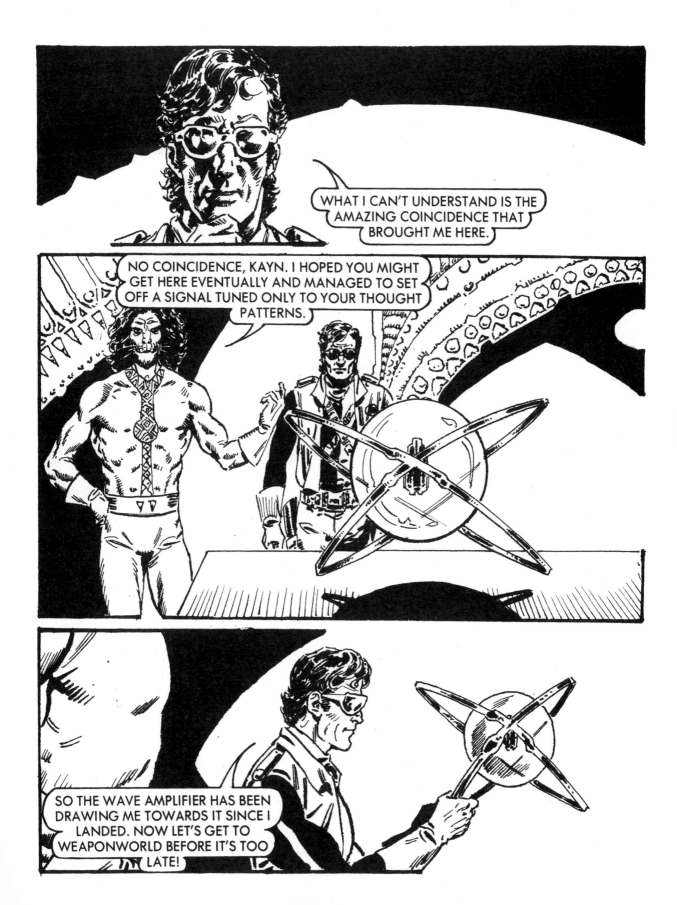

USING THE RAIDERS' AIRBOAT, THEY SPED THROUGH THE SHADOWS TO THE SPACEPORT . . .

THE SHIP ROARED INTO SPACE.

THAT'S ALL WE NEED—MORE RAIDERS.

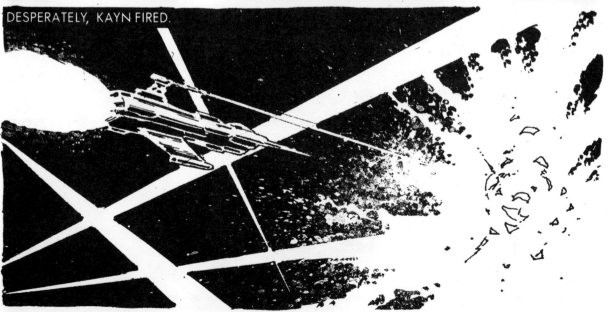

DESPERATELY, KAYN FIRED.

THE NUCLEAR LANDING ENGINE FLEW INTO THE MIDST OF THE FLEET.

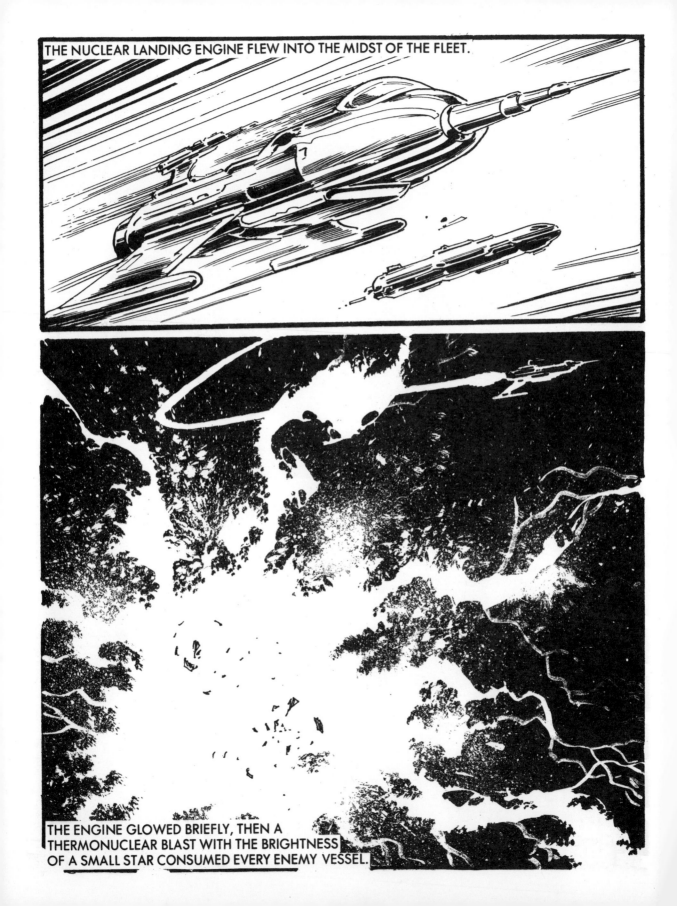

THE ENGINE GLOWED BRIEFLY, THEN A THERMONUCLEAR BLAST WITH THE BRIGHTNESS OF A SMALL STAR CONSUMED EVERY ENEMY VESSEL.

AS THEY DREW CLOSER TO WEAPONWORLD, THEY
CAME ACROSS THE TERRIFYING RESULTS OF
ALTA'S HANDIWORK; WORLDS WRECKED AND
RACES SLAUGHTERED.

KAYN! I'M GETTING A RETURN SIGNAL! THEY'RE TRYING TO CLEAR A PATH FOR US. THEY REMEMBER US!
ONE MISTAKE AND I KILL A LOT OF LIVING BEINGS.
YOU DID IT, KAYN!
LET'S SEE IF I CAN BRING HER DOWN WITHOUT THE LANDING ENGINE NOW.

FORCESHIELD WILL RESIST UP TO 72.12 PROTON BLAST . . . OUR PROTON BLASTERS CAN PRODUCE 70.02. WE MIGHT BE ABLE TO WEAKEN ONE SPOT ENOUGH TO CRASH THROUGH.

ALL PROTON CANNON AT MAXIMUM.

MAX LATCH . . . TOTAL FORCE OF JUST UNDER 70.00 . . . WE SHOULD BREAK THROUGH.

KAYN'S SHIP STREAKED LOW OVER THE JUMBLE OF HORRIFIC WEAPONS.

THEY LEAPT FROM COVER—

HIS BLASTER WAS INEFFECTIVE AGAINST THE ADAMANTIUM SHELL OF THE ROBOT KILLER.

TOO CLOSE . . .

AS KAYN MADE A RUN FOR IT, SOMETHING CAUGHT HIS EYE.

A MATTER CONVERTER! IT'S BEEN DEACTIVATED. IF I CAN LINK IT TO THE POWER CARTRIDGE IN MY BLASTER . . .

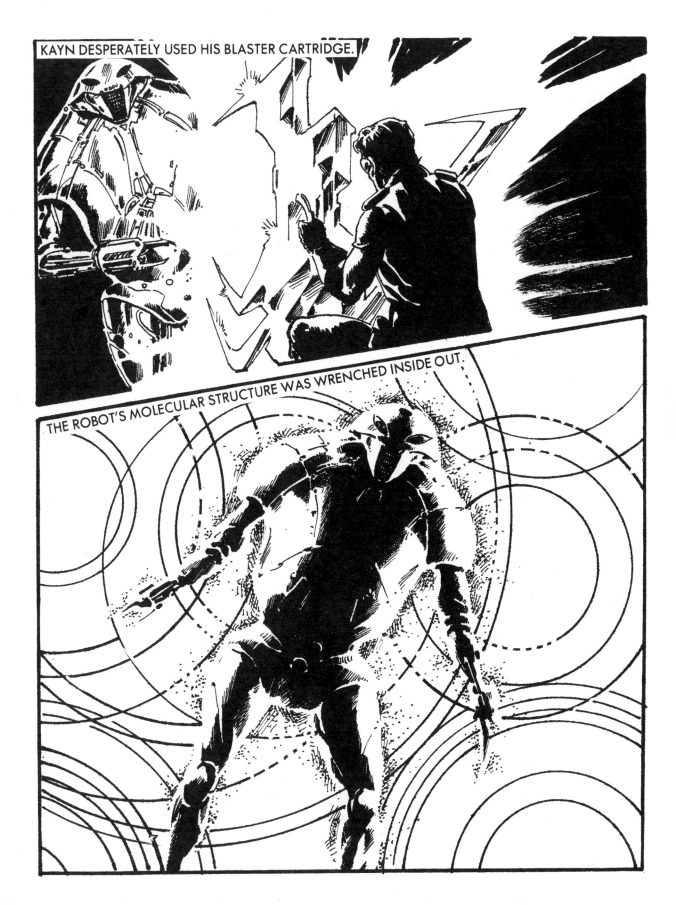

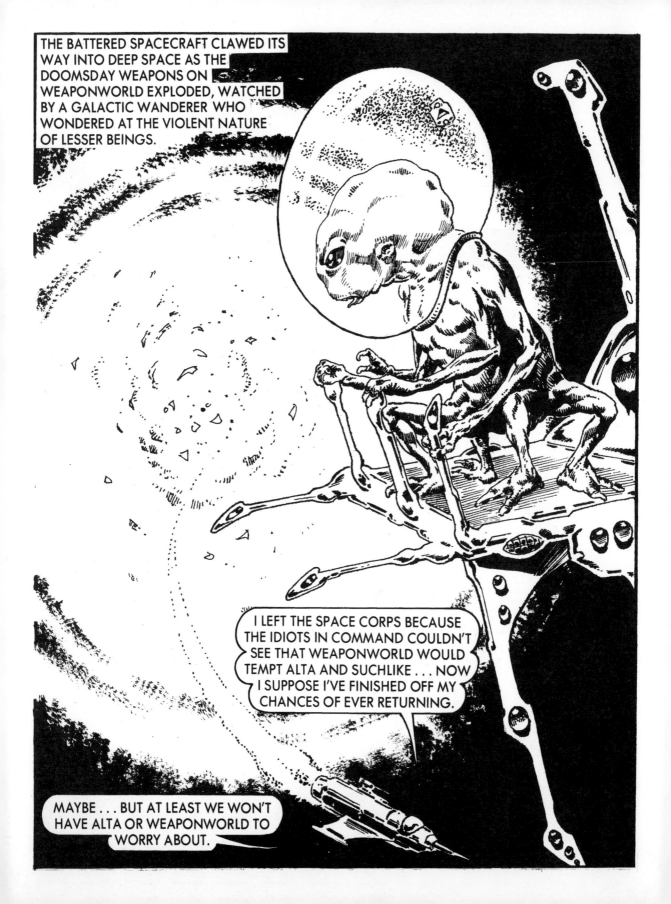

Cover by Keith Robson

JAWS OF DEATH

ON CONTROL WHEEL Z409, THE DUTY CONTROLLER WAS IN COMMUNICATION WITH THE FREIGHTER, SILVER LADY.

Z409 TO SILVER LADY. YOUR COURSE IS 7N240.1. SPEED IS WARP 3. SOLAR STORMS, FORCE 3 PREDICTED FOR SECTION X24.3.

SOME HOURS LATER, CAPTAIN PHIL COLLINS WAS SUMMONED BY THE COMMANDER OF THE FEDERATION SPACE NAVY.

COLLINS, YOU HAVE BEEN ASSIGNED TO FIND OUT WHAT HAPPENED TO THE SILVER LADY. SHE IS THE SEVENTH EARTH SHIP TO DISAPPEAR. KEEP IN CONSTANT COMMUNICATION.

CAPTAIN PHIL COLLINS, OF THE SPECIAL SPACE EXECUTIVE, WAS A SOLITARY OPERATOR — A MAN TRAINED TO ACT ON HIS OWN.

WELL, HERE GOES — THE INFORMATION FROM THE COMPUTER SHOULD TAKE ME TO THE HEART OF THE TROUBLE.

COLLINS PUT HIS SHIP INTO HYPERDRIVE, AND SET THE COURSE.

WHEN COLLINS REACHED THE SILVER LADY'S LAST KNOWN POSITION —

I'M IN TROUBLE. NO RESPONSE FROM THE SHIP'S CONTROLS.

ALL SYSTEMS MALFUNCTIONING . . . REPEAT . . . ALL . . .

ON BOARD Z409 —

COLLINS HAS DISAPPEARED FROM THE SAME SECTOR, SIR.

EMERGENCY WARNING — ALL SHIPS TO AVOID THE FOLLOWING TRIANGLE OF COORDINATES . . .

ALTHOUGH OFF THE SCREENS, COLLINS WAS STILL ALIVE.

THAT BRIGHT ASTEROID — IT SEEMS TO BE PULLING ME TOWARDS IT.

ONCE THE SHIP HAD SETTLED —

NOW TO INVESTIGATE.

COLLINS JETTED ACROSS TO THE NEAREST SPACESHIP.

THE POWER SOURCE MUST BE AT THE CENTRE OF THE ASTEROID BECAUSE THERE WAS A STRONG MAGNETIC FIELD AROUND IT.

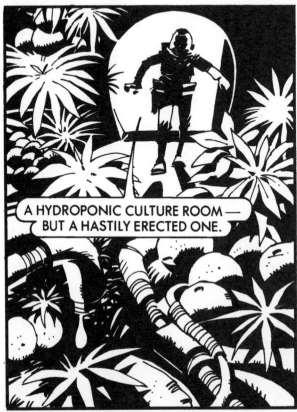

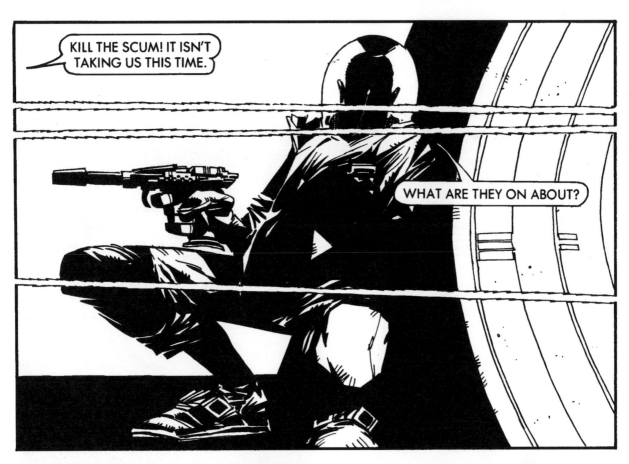

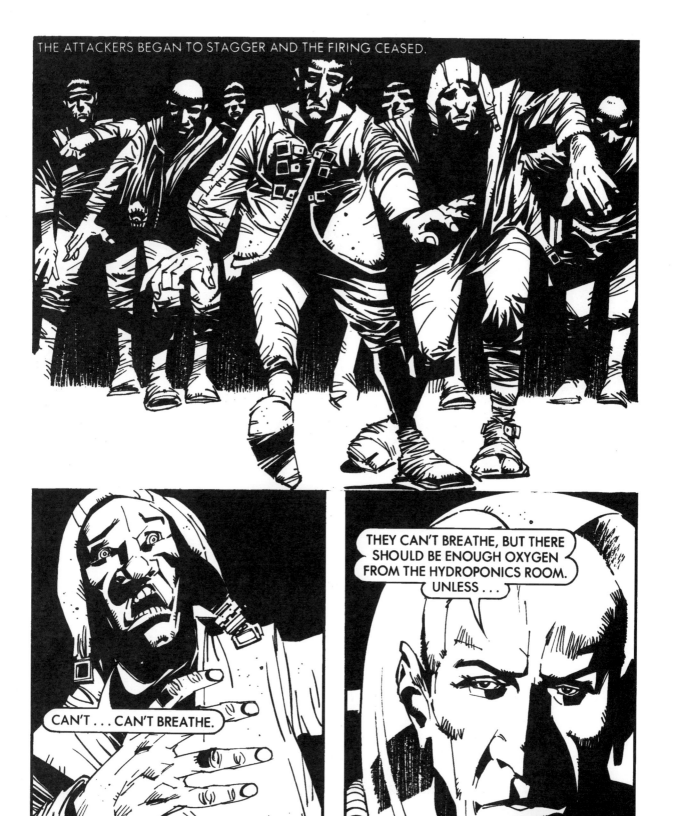

A LASER BEAM FRACTURED AN OXYGEN PIPE.

AIR CAME FLOODING BACK ONCE COLLINS HAD REPAIRED THE PIPE.

FIGHTING AGAINST TIME, THE CREW MEMBERS LINKED UP THE POWER SOURCES TO ONE OF THE BIGGEST FREIGHTERS.

AS THE CREW SCRAMBLED ABOARD THE FREIGHTER, THE "NIBBLER" STARTED ITS WORK.

MAXIMUM POWER — OPEN THROTTLES!

THE GIANT FREIGHTER PULLED FREE FROM THE ASTEROID AS THE VARDA KILLERS TRIED TO SEVER THE CABLES.

WE'RE FREE!

COLLINS JETTED UP TO THE CONTROL ROOM, HIGH UP ABOVE THE JAWS.

THERE MUST BE ANOTHER WAY IN.

THE TAIL . . . AND I KNOW A WAY TO SLOW THIS THING DOWN.

THAT'S THE FURNACE SHUT OFF! RAPID COOLING SHOULD CAUSE THE FURNACE WALL TO CRACK — THEN SOMETHING WILL HAPPEN.

THE SUPERHEATED ALLOY FURNACE WALL CRACKED AS THE CONSTITUENT METALS CONTRACTED AT DIFFERING TEMPERATURES.

THE VARDA WILL BE TOO CONCERNED TO NOTICE ME, AND I'LL GET OUT.

ALARMS SHRILLED AND THE VARDA RETURNED TO THE NIBBLER.

MALFUNCTION — RETURN TO THE HOMEBASE.

IN THE CONFUSION, COLLINS SLIPPED AWAY —

WE'LL FOLLOW THE NIBBLER. IT'S BADLY DAMAGED SO IT WILL HAVE TO RETURN TO BASE.

UNDER ANTI-SENSOR SHROUDS THE FREIGHTER FOLLOWED THE NIBBLER.

MANY SPACIALS LATER —

COMP — GIVE A RUN-DOWN ON PLANET.

COLLINS MANAGED TO KEEP THE CRAFT ON AN EVEN KEEL.

FAR OFF, TWO VARDA WATCHED —

ALIEN CRAFT IN SECTOR 2-ZERO — INVESTIGATE.

MIRACULOUSLY, NOBODY HAD BEEN KILLED IN THE CRASH.

I'LL TAKE THESE MEN AND HAVE A LOOK ROUND.

KEEP IN TOUCH OVER THE INTERCOM — WE'LL BE ON STANDBY.

THE MACHINES BATTERED THEIR WAY INTO THE CITY.

THE NIBBLER DESCENDED ON THE MACHINE ARMY.

QUICKLY — INSIDE THIS PLACE.

THE DIGGING MACHINE SEVERED THE MAIN POWER CABLE . . .

THE RESULTANT LOSS OF POWER ALLOWED COLLINS AND THE OTHERS TO ESCAPE.

THE NIBBLER'S HERE. WE'RE PULLING BACK.

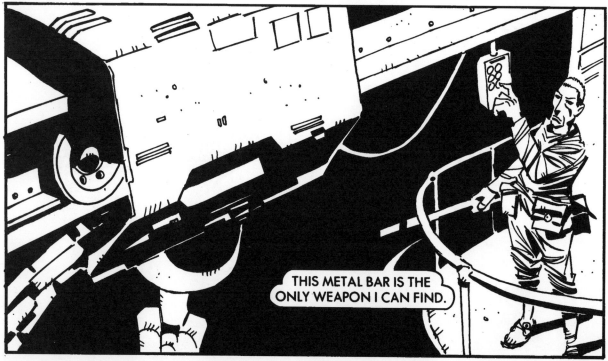

THEY FOUGHT THEIR WAY TO THE ENTRY PORT —

VARDON SAID THIS MARK II WAS AN IMPROVED VERSION — LET'S TRY IT OUT.

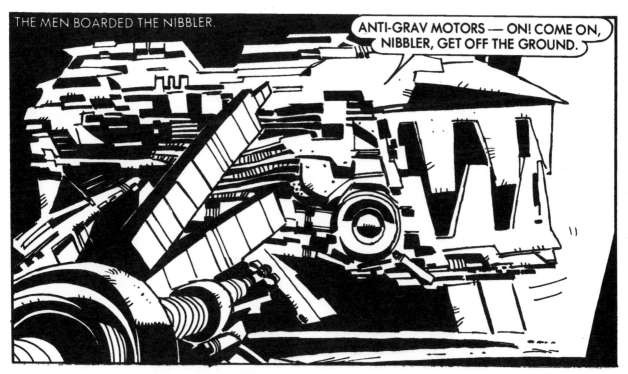

THE MEN BOARDED THE NIBBLER.

ANTI-GRAV MOTORS — ON! COME ON, NIBBLER, GET OFF THE GROUND.

MEANWHILE, THE OTHER NIBBLER DECIMATED THE MAKESHIFT ARMOUR.

THERE'S TWO OF THEM COMING FOR US NOW!

A DEFOLIATOR KEPT UP A FUTILE CHALLENGE.

YOUR PUNY FLAMETHROWER IS OF LITTLE USE TO YOU!

WITH A DEAFENING CRASH THE TWO GIANTS COLLIDED.

COLLINS BACKED OFF, AND ATTACKED VARDON FROM UNDERNEATH.

FOOL, LET ME TAKE OVER.

LOCKED IN A DEATH STRUGGLE, THE TWO NIBBLERS PLUNGED TO THE GROUND . . .

. . . AND VARDON'S BATTLEFLEET.

DID YOU SEE THAT — STRAIGHT INTO VARDON'S FLEET! WE'D BETTER GET COLLINS OUT OF THERE.

THE EARTH CREWS SWARMED TOWARDS THE VARDA —

IT'S THE ATOMIC PILE, SIR, FOR MELTING DOWN THE METAL — THE COMPUTER ASSESSES A CRITICAL SITUATION IN TEN MINUTES.

CAN WE STOP IT?

THERE ISN'T TIME — LET'S GET EVERYBODY OUT OF HERE.

VARDON, TOO, HAD ESCAPED DEATH. HE DRAGGED HIMSELF TO THE DOOR . . .

FOOL, HE NEVER WAS ANY GOOD.

ONCE ALL THE MEN WERE ON BOARD THE SHIP —

STAND BY. LET'S GET THIS THING OFF THE GROUND.

ALL ENERGISERS ON MAXIMUM.

COLLINS PUT THE SPACESHIP INTO BLAST OFF.

EVEN AS THEY CLEARED THE PLANET A ROARING FIREBALL BATHED THE STERILE GLOBE.

SET A COURSE FOR THAT ASTEROID WE WERE CAUGHT ON. IT IS OUR ONLY CHANCE.

ONLY SKILFUL FLYING KEPT VARDON AT BAY.

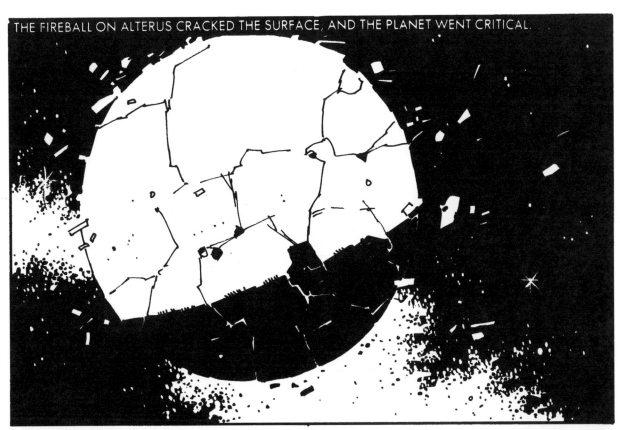
THE FIREBALL ON ALTERUS CRACKED THE SURFACE, AND THE PLANET WENT CRITICAL.

. . . AND EXPLODED INTO A BILLION PIECES.

VARDON'S FOLLOWED US . . .
MY TIMING HAS TO BE SPOT ON —
OR WE'RE ALL DEAD.

COLLINS HAD TO BE OUTWITH THE ASTEROID'S WEAK GRAVITATIONAL PULL.

COLLINS' TIMING WAS PERFECT. HIS CRAFT WAS FREE OF THE ASTEROID WHEN, DEPRIVED OF ITS POWER SOURCE ON ALTERUS, IT IMPLODED, SUCKING IN VARDON'S CRAFT.

MEET THE ARTIST:

NEIL ROBERTS

TELL US HOW YOU FIRST VENTURED INTO COMIC ART?

As a child I would get the comics weekly thanks to my parents and grandparents — *Beano*, *The Dandy*, *Nutty* and *Dan Dare* — and I would often copy out pages and panels from them, so it was all funny faces, aircraft and spaceships. Then, as a teenager I was drawing comic strips for fanzines — war/action stories and Sci-Fi stuff. What I really enjoyed was the sheer rigour of drawing, challenging myself to be competent enough to draw anything from any angle.

DO YOU HAVE ANY FORMAL TRAINING?

Yes and no.

Yes, I went to art college but, no, it wasn't an art education in a strictly formal/classical sense. The real bulk of my training came after I entered the video game industry, as they had a very strong need for traditional skills that weren't taught in any academic institution. Surrounded by other like-minded artists, animators and designers, we would regularly attend and organise life drawing sessions or 'en plein air' assignments — pushing each other to try our best. Having said that, as an artist I feel I've never stopped learning. The simple practice of making art is a constant classroom in itself.

WHERE WILL PEOPLE BEST RECOGNISE YOUR WORK?

My work has most widely been seen on the covers of the New York Times best-selling series *Horus Heresy* books from Black Library. I've also produced covers for *2000 AD*, various history books and wargaming magazines — I'm also particularly proud of my *Commando* comics work.

WHAT IS YOUR DREAM PROJECT?

Something epic with spaceships, robots and aliens — and an intimate and sensitive sense of character. Not much then!

IS THERE A PARTICULAR GENRE YOU PREFER TO WORK IN?

Science Fiction — because you can let your imagination run wild!

WHO/WHAT INSPIRES YOUR WORK MOST?

Easy. Ian Kennedy.
Ian is a brilliant artist, a lovely person, generous with his knowledge and has a solid and highly respected career. A good artist should inspire by example and he's one of the best.

On a broader level, I'm inspired by all art, whether it be classical, eastern, pop, modern or anything else. I see art as a progression, so I'd like to stay as open to inspiration as possible. Any piece of culture — art, games, movies, music and books has the potential to spark an idea or inspire a mood.

WHAT IS YOUR FAVOURITE PIECE OF ART BY SOMEONE ELSE?

I can touch upon two pieces of art that have stuck with me. Ian Kennedy's *Dan Dare* and *Eagle* work — a combination of amazing draughtsmanship and bold colour choices that still astounds me. And the original *Warhammer 40,000 Rogue Trader* cover art by John Sibbick. I'd never seen such grim and futile heroism in a painting before, plus all the weird and cool space armour instantly grabbed my attention and has never let go.

WHAT IS YOUR FAVOURITE PIECE OF YOUR OWN ART?

None. The next piece will always be better.

HOW IS STUDIO LIFE?

I love working in my studio, everything is geared towards inspiration — shelves of reference books, plastic models, headphones to tune the world out, a smart TV to stream films/boxsets. I'm lucky that my family are into it too, they see it as quite cool and rather strange, but the practice really works.

WHAT TOOL OF THE CRAFT CAN'T YOU DO WITHOUT?

Eyes — I'd literally be lost without them. Seriously though, a sketchbook — scribbling ideas down whenever inspiration hits is always the most exciting moment.

ROBOTS OR ALIENS?

Robots. At least they have an off switch.

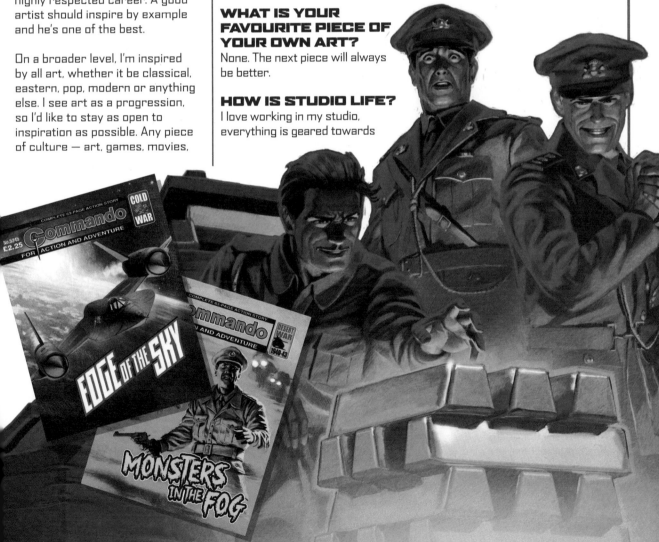

'Operation Overkill' Artist
ENRIQUE ALCATENA

An Argentinean comic artist, Alcatena self-trained before starting his career in the 1970s at Ediciones Récord and DC Thomson, for which he drew several issues of *Starblazer*.

Since then, Alcatena has also done work for Marvel and DC Comics, including 'Adventures of Superman', 'Batman: Legends of the Dark Knight', 'Doom 2099' and 'Conan' #10-11. He currently lives in Argentina.

'Jaws of Death' Artist
MICK MᶜMAHON

Best known for his work on *2000 AD*, Mick McMahon is a British comic artist, penciller and inker. Early in his career, McMahon was given the task of drawing the first ever Judge Dredd for publication in 1977, closely imitating intended artist Carlos Ezquerra's style. Since then, McMahon has developed his own signature style, working on other *2000 AD* series 'ABC Warriors', as well as for other publishers like DC Comics and Titan.

HERITAGE COMICS

RAMSEY'S RAIDERS GRAPHIC NOVEL VOLUME 1
£14.99

Discover the first two issues of the classic Ramsey's Raiders comic series about a rag-tag team of maverick soldiers operating behind enemy lines, reformatted in graphic novel size with full-colour pages.

RAMSEY'S RAIDERS GRAPHIC NOVEL VOLUME 2
£14.99

Collecting the third and fourth issues of Ramsey's Raiders from the weekly *Commando* comics, the original black-and-white artwork has been reborn with eruptions of eye-catching colour, and blown up to full-sized graphic novel format!

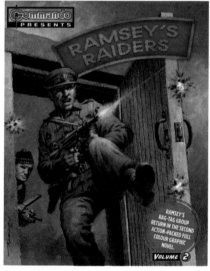

THE ART OF IAN KENNEDY
£40

Celebrating 70 years of Ian Kennedy's artwork for DC Thomson.

Celebrating 70 years of Ian Kennedy's artwork for DC Thomson in the company's first-ever 'Art of' book. Collecting rarely seen original pages and sketches from Kennedy's illustrious career at DC Thomson, from the pages of publications as diverse as *The Topper* to *Warlord*, *Lucky Charm* to *Starblazer*, set out chronologically from the 1950s to the present day, with a glimpse into the future!

COMMANDO COMICS
£2.25 each or to SUBSCRIBE AND SAVE go to commandocomics.com

Commando delivers four issues of action and adventure filled war comics every two weeks, with two brand-new military themed stories and two reprinted classics from the DC Thomson Archives. Established in 1961, *Commando* is Britain's longest-running war comic.

RAMSEY'S RAIDERS VOL.1 & 2 PACK
£25

This great-value pack contains four Ramsey's Raiders classic stories set out in two rowdy graphic novels.

www.dcthomsonshop.co.uk   commandoqueries@dctmedia.co.uk